Popular Teaching Resources

Canadian
Government

Grades **4-6**

Printed in China

Contents

Project Ideas

Biography

Take a Look!

Tests, Self-Evaluation, and Answers

Guidelines for Use

This resource book contains three sections:

- Core Units
- Project Ideas
- Tests, Self-Evaluation, and Answers

Each **Core Unit** is made up of an information sheet and follow-up worksheet(s). You will see that in most units, "Name", "Date", and the unit topic appear in each follow-up worksheet, so that each one can stand on its own. Depending on how you structure your lessons, you may want to give your students both the fact sheet and worksheet(s) at the same time. Alternatively, you may want to give just the information sheet one day, ask your students to underline keywords or key facts, or take notes as you talk about the subject, and then give them a worksheet the next day as a quiz.

The **Project Ideas** give students the opportunity to do some independent research and then share it with the rest of the class. You may also want to adapt them to be up to date with current events.

There are two separate **Tests** which you can give to your students. Depending on whether or not you teach all the units in this book, you may want to adapt each test to suit what you've taught. You may also want to let your students use the **Self-Evaluation** sheet as a study guide.

Happy teaching!

Grades 4-6

Canadian Government

Core Units

The Canadian Government

What kind of government is Canada? Is it a monarchy, where the ruler is a king or queen? Or is it a republic, which is a country without a monarch? Canada is neither one of these. Canada is a **constitutional monarchy**, meaning that the monarch (Queen of England) is the head of state, but her powers are limited by the Constitution, the set of laws that govern the country. In a constitutional monarchy, the head of government is the Prime Minister. The monarch's role is mostly symbolic, to carry out traditional and ceremonial duties.

Canada is also a **federation**. This means that the country is formed by a group of "members". The members in Canada are the ten provinces and three territories.

Canada is also a **democracy**. This means that citizens have the right to choose their government. They do this by electing representatives to act on their behalf. The representatives who win the most votes from the public will then help solve problems by making laws.

The supreme law of Canada is the *Charter of Rights and Freedoms*, which protects the basic rights and freedoms of all Canadians. For example, Canadians have the right to vote and have freedom of religion. The Charter also makes **bilingualism** and **multiculturalism** official policies in the country. This is why Canada has two official languages, French and English. It is also why school boards provide free heritage classes to students of various ethnic backgrounds so that they can learn the language of their culture.

I speak Chinese at home.

I come from Greece!

I can speak Portuguese!

My family is from Japan.

The Canadian Government

A. Match each of these with its meaning.

| A | having two official languages in the country |

| B | system of government where citizens have the right to choose their government |

| C | country made up of "members" such as provinces and territories |

| D | having many cultures in one country |

1. democracy _____   2. federation _____

3. bilingualism _____   4. multiculturalism _____

B. Answer these questions.

1. What is a "constitutional monarchy"?

   _____

   _____

2. In a constitutional monarchy, what is the role of the monarch?

   _____

   _____

3. What is the purpose of the *Charter of Rights and Freedoms*?

   _____

   _____

The Canadian Government

Look at this map of Canada. Use the short forms to help you write down the names of the 13 members of Canada's federation. Then finish what Cindy says.

CANADA

"Members" of Canada's Federation

Provinces

BC: _____   QB: _____

AB: _____   NFL: _____

SK: _____   PEI: _____

MB: _____   NB: _____

ON: _____   NS: _____

Territories

YT: _____

NT: _____

NU: _____

> *There's a total of _____ provinces and _____ territories in Canada's federation.*

The Canadian Government

Imagine the Queen is visiting your community and you are going to show her around. Think of two places, paste or draw a picture of each, and then write down why you want to show the two places to the Queen.

Places I Want to Show the Queen

I'm coming to Canada!

Suggestions

- museum
- provincial park
- City Hall/Town Hall
- heritage/historic site

Three Levels of Government

The Canadian government is made up of three levels: federal, provincial/territorial, and municipal.

The federal government looks after the affairs of the country. It is responsible for things such as the environment, fisheries, forestry, import and export, income tax, national defence, citizenship and immigration, and relations with other countries. The federal government consists of people from every province and territory in Canada, and the head of the government is the Prime Minister.

The provincial/territorial government looks after the affairs of the province or territory. It is responsible for things such as charities, hospitals, the police, drivers' licences, birth, death, and marriage certificates, property and civil rights, and education. The provincial/territorial government consists of people from different parts of the province or territory. The head of the provincial/territorial government is the Premier.

The municipal government looks after the affairs of the city, town, village, county, or district. It is responsible for things such as water supply, sewage, roads, sidewalks, street lights, snow removal, city parks and playgrounds, libraries, and school boards. The municipal government consists of people from different parts of the community, and the head of the government is the Mayor.

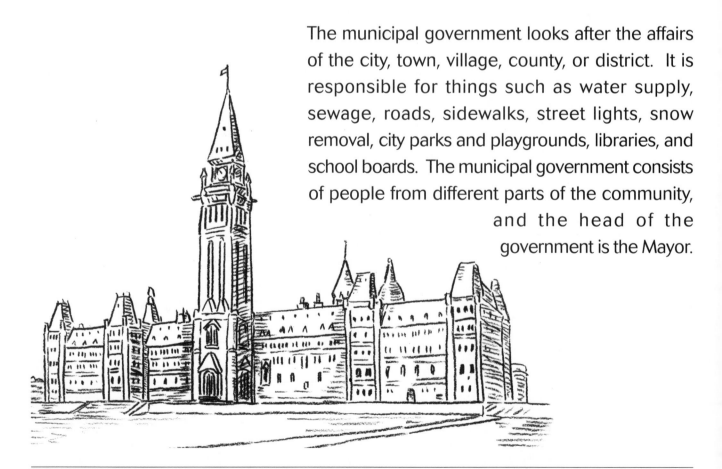

Three Levels of Government

A.   Write "T" for "True" or "F" for "False".

1.   The head of the federal government is the Premier.   _____

2.   The head of the municipal government is the Mayor.   _____

3.   The Prime Minister is the head of Canada.   _____

4.   Our city parks and playgrounds are looked after by the
     provincial/territorial government.   _____

5.   Things like sewage, roads, and snow removal are the
     responsibilities of the municipal government.   _____

B.   Write "federal", "provincial/territorial", or "municipal". Then think of one more example for each one.

1.      • birth, death, and marriage certificates

     • _____

2.   • citizenship and immigration

     • _____

3.      • ETS, the Edmonton Transit System

     • _____

How the Government Gets Paid: Taxes

Think of some of the things that we may take for granted, like health care, education, social assistance, and parks and recreation. The government needs money to pay for all these. That is why we pay taxes.

In Canada, we pay the government in several ways:

Income Tax
- money we "give up" from our salary when we have a job
- government's biggest source of revenue
- used to fund programs/services administered at the federal level

Sales Tax
- money collected from the things we buy
- examples: Goods and Services Tax (GST), Provincial Sales Tax (PST)
- used to fund programs/services administered at federal and provincial levels

Property Tax
- money collected from homeowners and land owners
- collected by the municipal government for local programs/services

Government
- education
- health care
- social assistance
- recreation

A country's tax system is not only its way of making money, but also a reflection of its values. The fact that our government uses taxes to help the poorer sections of society, for example, shows it cares about the less fortunate. And remember, we have a say in how our money should be used. If we want a government that uses our money wisely, we had better pay attention to what the different political parties say about their budget during election times!

How the Government Gets Paid: Taxes

A. **Write the type of tax that each person is talking about.**

1.

Look at the cost of this jacket! It's so expensive. And don't forget you have to pay taxes on top of the price. You had better think twice before buying it.

_____

2.

I'm not going to buy a house yet. I might have enough for a down payment, but I don't think I'll have enough to pay the tax.

_____

3.

Yes! I'm getting my first paycheque! But wait...I see some deductions. They must be the tax that I need to pay.

_____

B. **Write down some of the things that we get by paying taxes.**

1. _____   2. _____

3. _____   4. _____

How the Government Gets Paid: Taxes

Fill in the blanks with the given words to see what taxes pay for.

| safety | sidewalks | street lights | books | recreation |

1. How do taxes help us get to school? Well, for those of us who...

   a. **take the school bus:**

      the government covers the cost of maintaining school buses and

      meeting _____ standards.

   b. **walk:**

      the government maintains the _____ that we use on a daily basis.

   c. **get a ride from our parents:**

      the government maintains the roads, _____ , and traffic lights in the city or town.

2. How do taxes make our community fun? They provide us with...

   a. **parks, playgrounds, and swimming pools**

      It takes people to keep _____ facilities in good shape, and the government is responsible for paying these people.

   b. **public libraries**

      Libraries purchase new _____ by getting funding from the government.

How the Government Gets Paid: Taxes

Look through some used newspapers and magazines at home. Find pictures of things that you think are paid for by taxes, and make a collage of them below.

Political Parties in Canada

Canada has a very diverse population, which creates a rich mix of viewpoints among citizens. That is why there are so many political parties in Canada.

What is a political party? It is an organization with the goal of forming a government. Every party has its own "vision", a set of ideas that its members believe in. If the party wins enough votes from the public, then it is in charge of governing the people.

In Canada, political parties exist at the federal and provincial/territorial levels. For example, if the Liberal Party wins the *provincial* election in Ontario, then it will be the governing party of the province. But if the Conservative Party wins the *federal* election, then it will be the governing party of Canada.

There are 15 registered federal political parties. Below are the five biggest ones:

Bloc Québécois (founded in 1991)
- promotes the interests of Quebec citizens and their independence from the rest of Canada

Conservative Party of Canada (founded in 2003)
- generally does not like to spend money on social programs and services, spends more money on the military and promotes closer ties with the U.S. government

Green Party of Canada (founded in 1983)
- practises "green politics" by solving societal problems from an environmental standpoint, and rose to prominence in recent years

Liberal Party of Canada (founded in 1867)
- generally has a balanced approach to policies, is a strong proponent of social programs and services (e.g. health care), favours balanced budgets rather than run the risk of having a deficit

New Democratic Party (founded in 1961)
- favours many social programs and services, is a strong advocate for peace and the environment, but its policies tend to cost the government a lot of money, resulting in a deficit

Political Parties in Canada

Finish each sentence with the correct ending.

- win votes from the population
- Canada will have a Liberal government
- has a diverse population with a variety of viewpoints
- an organization with the goal of forming a government
- then it means the New Democratic Party has won the federal election

1. A political party is _____ .

2. In order to be in charge of government, a political party needs to

   _____ .

3. If the Liberal Party wins the federal election, then _____

   _____ .

4. There are many political parties in Canada because the country

   _____ .

5. If the Prime Minister belongs to the New Democratic Party, _____

   _____ .

Political Parties in Canada

Below are some past and present Canadian politicians. Use the library and/or online resources to find out their political parties, and a few points about their work. Then find and paste a picture for each one.

1.

   John A. Macdonald (1815–1891)

   Political party: *Conservative Party*

   - *first Prime Minister of Canada*
   - *built the Canadian Pacific Railway*

2.

   Pierre Trudeau (1919–2000)

   Political party: _____

   - _____
   - _____

3.

   Sheila Copps (1952–   )

   Political party: _____

   - _____
   - _____

4.

   Elizabeth May (1954–   )

   Political party: _____

   - _____
   - _____

Political Parties in Canada

Get into a group of four or five and form a new political party. Come up with a name and decide on the official colours for it. Then design and colour its logo. Finally, think about how your party would govern Canada and describe your party's "vision".

> *Visit the websites of these current political parties to get ideas!*

www.ndp.ca
www.liberal.ca   www.conservative.ca
www.greenparty.ca   www.blocquebecois.org

Our **Political Party**

Vision _____

_____

_____

Elections in Canada

In Canada, people in charge of government are elected by the citizens. During an election, a candidate is voted into office to represent the people of a specific area. In federal and provincial elections, this area is called a **riding**. In a municipal election, this area is called a **ward**. In territorial elections, however, there are no ridings or wards.

In a federal election, we elect the **Prime Minister** and Members of Parliament **(MPs)**. They meet in the House of Commons to debate laws.

In a provincial/territorial election, we elect the **Premier** and members of the provincial/territorial legislature. In most provinces and in all territories, members of the legislature are called **Members of the Legislative Assembly (MLAs)**. In some provinces, they have different names. In Ontario, for example, they are called Members of Provincial Parliament **(MPPs)**.

In federal and provincial elections, the candidates representing the different ridings each belong to a political party. If the majority of ridings are won by candidates belonging to the Green Party, for example, then the party becomes the governing party, and its leader becomes the Prime Minister or the Premier.

In municipal elections, we elect a **Mayor, City Councillors,** and **School Trustees**. Unlike candidates at the provincial and federal levels, most candidates at the municipal level do not belong to any political party.

So when do we have elections? Federal and provincial elections happen at least every five years, while municipal elections happen about every three years.

Federal
- ✔ Prime Minister
- ✔ MPs: Members of Parliament

Provincial/Territorial
- ✔ Premier
- ✔ MLAs: Members of the Legislative Assembly
- ✔ MPPs: Members of Provincial Parliament
- ✔ MNAs: Members of the National Assembly
- ✔ MHAs: Members of the House of Assembly

Municipal
- ✔ Mayor
- ✔ City Councillors
- ✔ School Trustees

Elections in Canada

Underline the correct answers.

1. In federal and provincial elections, the area represented by an electoral candidate is called a **ward / riding** .

2. In a municipal election, the area represented by an electoral candidate is called a **ward / riding** .

3. In a federal election, we elect the **Prime Minister / Premier** .

4. In a provincial/territorial election, we elect the **Mayor / Premier** .

5. In most provinces and in all territories, members of the legislature are called **MPPs / MLAs** .

6. Unlike most provinces, members of the provincial legislature in Ontario are called **MPPs / MLAs** .

7. In a municipal election, the three different posts that we elect are the Mayor, City Councillors, and **MPPs / School Trustees** .

8. Most electoral candidates at the **provincial / municipal** level are not affiliated with any political party.

Elections in Canada

Read what Michelle and Julia say and complete this activity.

1.
> *Think back to the last municipal election in your community. Who was elected to be...*

a. your School Trustee?

_____

b. your City Councillor?

_____

c. your Mayor?

_____

Municipal Election

- Name of your ward:

_____

- Date of the election:

_____
day/month/year

2.

> *Now think back to the last provincial election in your province. Who, or what, was elected to be...*

Provincial Election

- Name of your riding:

_____

- Date of the election:

_____
day/month/year

a. your MP?

_____
(political party:)

b. the governing political party?

_____

c. the Premier?

_____

Elections in Canada

Your principal wants to make your school the best one in the city. He or she has come up with a plan: the school will elect a student who can make this come true.

Process of Election

1. Everyone from Grades 4 to 6 will give a speech of his or her ideas in front of the class.

2. Each person in the classroom, including the teacher, will vote for a "class representative": the student with the best ideas.

3. Students and teachers from Grades 4 to 6 will have a school assembly, where they will listen to the speeches from the class representatives.

4. The principal will ask all the students and teachers to vote for the one student with the greatest ideas.

5. The winner will see his or her ideas come true: teachers and the principal will use the ideas to make the school the best one in the city!

What ideas do you have and how will you present them? Write down your speech below. Here are some examples of ideas: How will you make the classroom a fun place to learn? What other after-school activities can you think of?

My Speech _____

_____

_____

_____

_____

_____

The Justice System in Canada

The justice system is made up of courts and judges. Their job is to interpret and apply the laws that have been passed by the federal, provincial/territorial, and municipal governments. There are four levels in the Canadian court system.

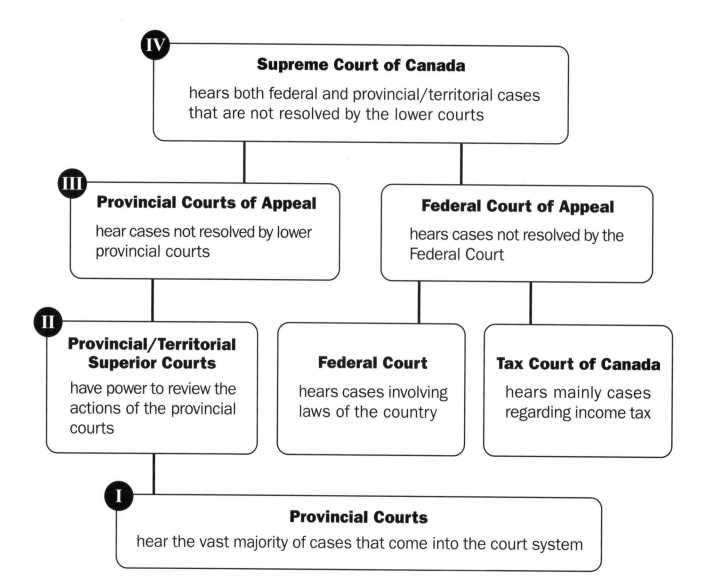

The Canadian Court System

IV **Supreme Court of Canada**
hears both federal and provincial/territorial cases that are not resolved by the lower courts

III **Provincial Courts of Appeal**
hear cases not resolved by lower provincial courts

Federal Court of Appeal
hears cases not resolved by the Federal Court

II **Provincial/Territorial Superior Courts**
have power to review the actions of the provincial courts

Federal Court
hears cases involving laws of the country

Tax Court of Canada
hears mainly cases regarding income tax

I **Provincial Courts**
hear the vast majority of cases that come into the court system

                    Canadian Government | G.4-6

The Justice System in Canada

Write the name of the court(s) for each description.

1. responsible for cases involving laws of the country

    _____

2. have power to review the actions of the provincial courts

    _____

3. responsible for the majority of cases in Canada

    _____

4. hears all the cases not resolved by the lower courts

    _____

5. deals with cases not resolved by the Federal Court

    _____

6. *These courts are in the second highest level of the system. They hear cases not settled by the lower provincial courts.*

    _____

7. *This court is in the same level as the Federal Court, but it deals mainly with income tax cases.*

    _____

Canadian Citizenship

If you were born in Canada, you are automatically a Canadian citizen. Canada is a country of many immigrants, however, and they became citizens because they fulfilled certain requirements, such as being 18 years of age or older, being able to speak English or French, and having lived in Canada for three years. They also attended the citizenship ceremony, where they took the Oath of Citizenship and sang "O Canada".

As a Canadian citizen, you are entitled to the rights and freedoms guaranteed by the government. At the same time, you have responsibilities too.

Examples of Rights and Freedoms

- **equality rights** – every citizen is equal regardless of race, ethnic origin, colour, religion, gender, age, or disability

- **mobility rights** – citizens have the right to work and live in another province/territory and to travel to a different country

- **freedom of expression** – citizens are free to express different ideas

- **freedom of religion** – citizens are free to practise different religions, like going to a temple, a synagogue, or a church

Examples of Responsibilities

You need to...

- obey the laws of Canada
- respect the rights and freedoms of fellow Canadian citizens
- protect the environment and the Canadian heritage
- eliminate discrimination and unfairness

Canadian Citizenship

Read each description and tell whether it is a "right", a "freedom", or a "responsibility". Then write down what it is from the given choices.

Rights and Freedoms	Responsibilities
• equality rights	• obeying Canadian laws
• mobility rights	• respecting others' rights
• freedom of expression	• protecting the environment
• freedom of religion	• eliminating discrimination

1. You recycle your cans, bottles, and newspapers, and compost your food scraps.

   _____ ; _____

2. Mrs. Hartley is not in town because she is travelling in South Africa.

   _____ ; _____

3. A Jewish teenager goes to his synagogue and a Sikh woman attends a public worship.

   _____ ; _____

4. Jonathan does not drink any beer at the party because he is not at the legal drinking age.

   _____ ; _____

Canadian Citizenship

See how much you know about the process of becoming a Canadian citizen. Circle the correct answers.

Becoming a Canadian Citizen

1. An adult who wants to become Canadian must _____ .

   A. be 18 years of age or older

   B. know someone who is Canadian

2. He or she must be able to _____ .

   A. speak English or French

   B. speak many languages

3. He or she must _____ .

   A. have a friend who lives in Canada

   B. be a permanent resident of Canada

4. He or she must _____ .

   A. have lived in Canada for one year

   B. have lived in Canada for three years

5. He or she must _____ .

   A. not go back to the country of his or her birth

   B. know his or her rights and responsibilities

Canadian Citizenship

Unscramble the letters to fill in the missing words in the Oath of Citizenship.

Oath of Citizenship

I affirm that I will be 1._____ and bear
fiahtufl

2._____ allegiance to Her Majesty
ruet

3._____ Elizabeth II, 4._____ of
Qneue   Qneue

Canada, Her Heirs and Successors, and that I will

faithfully observe the 5._____
lwsa

of Canada and fulfil my duties as a

Canadian 6._____ .
ctiienz

Canadian Citizenship

Use the given words to complete the national anthem of Canada.

glorious   guard   wide   hearts   native   love   free   North

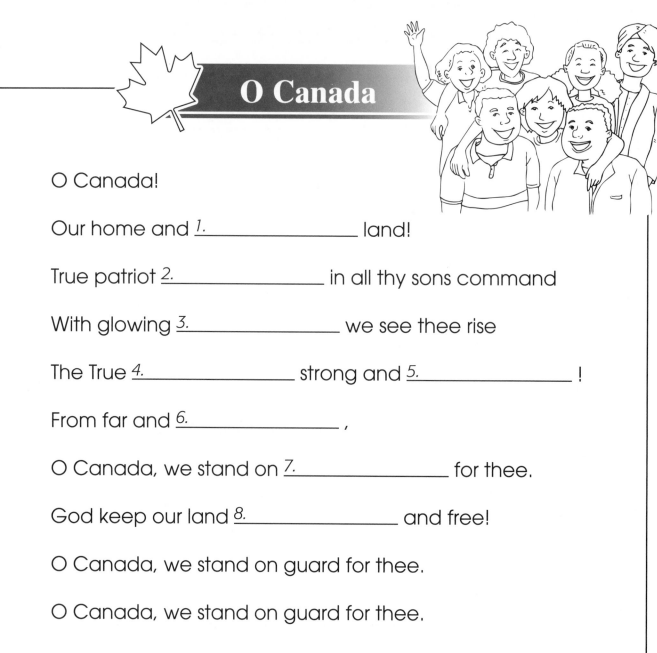

O Canada

O Canada!

Our home and <u>1.</u>_____ land!

True patriot <u>2.</u>_____ in all thy sons command

With glowing <u>3.</u>_____ we see thee rise

The True <u>4.</u>_____ strong and <u>5.</u>_____ !

From far and <u>6.</u>_____ ,

O Canada, we stand on <u>7.</u>_____ for thee.

God keep our land <u>8.</u>_____ and free!

O Canada, we stand on guard for thee.

O Canada, we stand on guard for thee.

30   Canadian Government | G.4-6

Canadian Citizenship

Something is missing on the Canadian flag. Look at Carly's shirt and read what she says to draw and colour it in.

Did you know that Canada's official colours are red and white? They're also the colours on our Maple Leaf flag!

The Canadian Flag

The Federal Government

The federal government of Canada is the central government of the country, with its buildings located in Ottawa, the country's capital. It is responsible for matters such as citizenship and immigration, the postal system, banking, laws that affect all Canadians, and foreign relations.

The federal government has a parliamentary system, which is why when we think of the federal government, we think of "Parliament".

Canada's Parliamentary System

Sovereign

This is the Governor General, representing the Queen of England. The role is ceremonial, but is above both the executive and legislative branches.

Executive Branch

- **Prime Minister and Cabinet**

  This is the head of government and his/her Cabinet of Ministers who help him/her run the country.

Legislative Branch

- **Senate ("upper house")**

  This body is responsible for passing laws. It is made up of senators selected by the Prime Minister and then appointed by the Governor General.

- **House of Commons ("lower house")**

  This is the major law-making body, where proposed laws are debated by Members of Parliament (MPs) elected by the public.

The Federal Government

Match each given word with the correct description.

> Senate   federal   Cabinet   Ottawa   Sovereign
> legislative   Prime Minister   executive

1. the head of government _____

2. the capital of Canada _____

3. having to do with all of Canada _____

4. the "upper house" of Parliament _____

5. helps the Prime Minister run the country _____

6. the branch made up of the Prime Minister and the Cabinet _____

7. the branch made up of the Senate and the House of Commons _____

8. the Governor General _____

The Federal Government

See if you can find answers to the following!
Use the library and/or online resources.

> *Here's a tip: you'll find many of the answers by visiting **www2.parl.gc.ca/parlinfo**. Once you're on the page, click on **"Parliament"** on the menu on the left-hand side, and then click on **"Canadian Parliamentary Trivia"**.*

Parliamentary Trivia

1. Who was Canada's first prime minister?   _____

2. Which prime minister served the longest?   _____

3. Which prime minister won the Nobel Peace Prize?   _____

4. Who was the first woman prime minister?   _____

5. Who was the first woman governor general?   _____

6. Who was the first woman senator?   _____

7. Who was the first woman MP?   _____

8. Which political party has been around the longest?   _____

9. Which political party has often been called "Canada's natural governing party"?   _____

The Federal Government

Read the clues to complete this crossword puzzle.

Names of Some Federal Departments

Across

A. develops environmental policies and protects wildlife

B. looks after the health care system

C. responsible for things like energy, forests, minerals, and metals: **Natural** _____

D. deals with matters regarding citizenship and immigration: **Citizenship and** _____

E. creates programs to help Canadians in school and at work:
    Human Resources and _____ **Development**

F. promotes Canadian arts and culture: **Canadian** _____

Down

1. ensures that the Canadian justice system is fair

2. responsible for Canada's international trade policies and relations with other countries:
    Foreign Affairs and _____ **Trade**

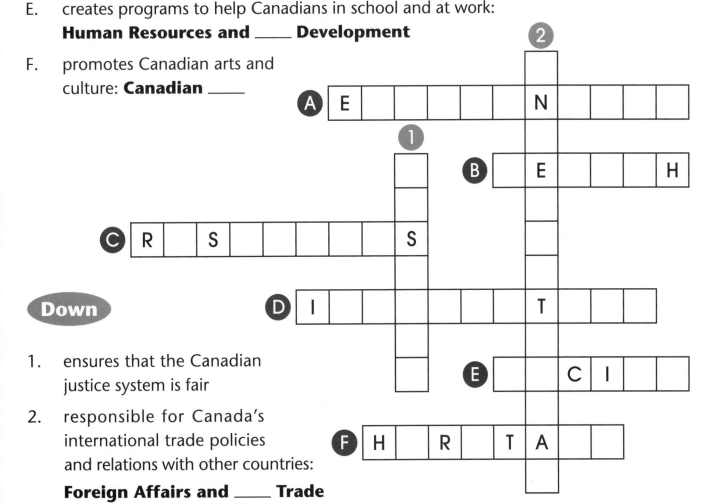

The House of Commons

The House of Commons, located inside the Parliament Buildings in Ottawa, is the centre of the federal government. It is where Members of Parliament (MPs) meet to debate issues and make laws.

Unlike the Senate, whose members are appointed by the Governor General, the House of Commons is an elected group made up of 301 members known as Members of Parliament (MPs). Each MP represents a district in Canada, called a "riding". Each MP also belongs to a political party. For example, if the majority of people in a riding elect a candidate from the Conservative Party, we say that the Conservative candidate has won a "seat" in the House of Commons.

Inside the "House" (as it is sometimes called), the party with the most "seats" is the governing party; its leader is the **Prime Minister** and its members are called **Government Members**. The party with the second-highest number of seats is called the **Official Opposition**; its leader is called the **Leader of the Official Opposition**. All the elected MPs not part of the governing party are called **Opposition Members**.

So what do MPs debate about inside the House of Commons? They debate important issues that affect Canadians. Each MP can also raise issues of concern to his or her riding and debate solutions with others to fix problems.

Since there is always debate inside the House of Commons, it needs someone to act as "umpire". That person is called the **Speaker**, who controls debates by calling on members to speak. The Speaker's authority is symbolized by the **Mace**, which is a ceremonial staff placed on the Table inside the House.

The House of Commons

Match the descriptions with the given words.

Speaker   Opposition Members

Official Opposition   Senate

Mace   House of Commons

1. the elected group of members in Parliament

    _____

2. the appointed group of members in Parliament

    _____

3. the person who controls the debates in the House

    _____

4. the party with the second-highest number of seats in the House

    _____

5. all the elected Members of Parliament (MPs) that are not part of the governing party

    _____

6. the ceremonial object that symbolizes the Speaker's authority

    _____

The House of Commons

Use Michelle's tip to help you label this close-up of the House of Commons Chamber. Then do some research to describe each of the following.

> *Go to Google. Click **"Images"** on the top left corner. Then in the search box, type these keywords: **"House of Commons"** and **"Chamber"** and **"CanadaInfo"**.*

House of Commons Chamber

A S_____ :

* _____

_____

B M_____ :

* _____

_____

C P_____ M_____ :

* _____

_____

D G_____ M_____ :

* _____

E Leader of the O_____ O_____ :

* _____

F O_____ M_____ :

* _____

The House of Commons

Use the library and/or online resources to find pictures of the Speaker's Mace. Make a sketch and colour it. Then write down some details below.

> *Go to Google. Click **"Images"** on the top left corner. Then in the search box, type these keywords: **"Speaker"** and **"Canada"** and **"Mace"**. Once you click on the correct image, you'll be on the Speaker's official website where you can also do some research!*

The Speaker's Mace

What the Mace Symbolizes

_____

_____

_____

_____

When the Mace is Used

_____

_____

_____

_____

How Laws are Made in Canada

Ever wondered how laws are made? They each begin as an idea, which becomes something called a "bill". A bill is like a rough draft that explains what the idea is. Every bill goes through a special review procedure called the "legislative process" before it becomes law.

During the legislative process, the bill is discussed and debated in the legislature. At the federal level, the legislature is the House of Commons. At the provincial/territorial level, it is the Legislative Assembly. At the municipal level, it is the Town Hall or City Hall.

The following shows how laws are made at the federal level:

 **Bill**   The **Legislative Process**

First reading (with no debate)

A bill is introduced to the legislature. In the federal parliament, first reading can occur in either the Senate or the House of Commons.

Second reading (debate begins but no amendments or changes yet)

The draft of the bill is read again. The bill is referred to a special committee, which may ask experts to provide information and make amendments. The bill is then sent back to the House for a vote on the amendments.

Third reading (final approval by members of the legislature)

Once the bill passes this third reading, then it is sent to the Senate where the process is repeated. If the bill passes the third reading there as well, then it is granted Royal Assent by the Governor General.

 **Law**

How Laws are Made in Canada

Answer the following questions.

1. What is a bill?

    _____

    _____

2. What is the legislative process?

    _____

    _____

3. What happens during the legislative process?

    _____

    _____

4. What is the legislature called in each of the following?

    a. Federal level: _____

    b. Provincial/Territorial level: _____

    c. Municipal level: _____

5. How many readings does a bill go through? What happens at the first reading?

    _____

    _____

    _____

    _____

How Laws are Made in Canada

A Simulation of the
Law-Making Process

Instructions for the Teacher:

1. Brainstorm with your class for "bill" ideas.

2. Give each student a cue card. Tell them that they are now "MPs". Ask them to come up with their own bills and write them down. Ask them to put their names on the cards.

3. Shuffle all the bills in a shoebox. Assign a group of students to be the "committee".

4. Randomly draw out a bill. Ask the MP who wrote it to read it in front of the class. This is the first reading, when the bill is introduced.

5. Take a vote and see if the majority wants the bill to have a second reading. If so, proceed to step 6. If not, draw out another bill for the process.

6. This is the second reading. Let the MP tell the class why his or her bill is a good idea. Then have all MPs debate what is good and bad about the bill. You are the Speaker, so decide whose turn it is to speak.

7. After a fair share of debate by everyone, take a vote to see if the majority wants the bill examined by the committee (from step 3). If so, proceed to step 8. If not, go on to step 12.

8. Allow members of the committee to improve the bill by making suggestions. Other MPs may talk quietly amongst themselves in the meantime.

9. Have the committee hand in their suggestions. Read each suggestion to the class and take a vote. Keep the suggestions that a majority of MPs agree upon.

10. This is the third reading. Read the improved bill to the entire class. Take a final vote from your MPs. If the majority agrees to pass the bill, it goes to you the Senate. If you decide to pass the bill, proceed to step 11. If not, tell the class why.

11. You now play the role of the Governor General by giving it Royal Assent.

12. Draw out another bill and repeat the process. Assign a different committee this time.

How Laws are Made in Canada

Bill

The following bill is proposed

by _____
your name

I propose that _____

_____

_____

_____ .

This bill is a good idea because _____

_____

_____

_____

_____

_____

_____ .

The Provincial/Territorial Government

The provincial/territorial government is responsible for matters such as education, energy, hospitals, liquor licence, and marriage licence. Its legislative building – or buildings – is located in the capital city of each province/territory. In Ontario, for example, the legislative building is located in Toronto; in British Columbia, the legislative buildings are located in Victoria.

Like the federal government, the provincial/territorial government has a Sovereign, a Legislature, and a Cabinet. The Sovereign is the Queen's representative (the Lieutenant Governor in provinces; the Commissioner in territories). The Legislature is called the "Legislative Assembly" or "Provincial Parliament" in most provinces/territories, and consists of elected MLAs/MPPs. The Cabinet consists of Ministers of the

The Provincial/Territorial Government

- **Sovereign** (Queen's representative)
  The Lieutenant Governor in provinces;
  The Commissioner in territories

- **Legislature**
  Consists of elected MLAs/MPPs

- **Cabinet**
  Consists of ministers of the province/territory, each selected by the Premier

province/territory, each selected by the Premier and responsible for a certain role in government. For example, the Minister of Education is responsible for education issues; the Minister of Health is responsible for health issues.

Each province is separated into electoral regions called "ridings", and one representative is elected into the Legislature from each of these ridings. Generally, each representative belongs to a political party (e.g. Liberal, Conservative, NDP). The party with the most representatives elected becomes the governing party and its leader becomes Premier. He or she governs for up to five years.

The Provincial/Territorial Government

Check the correct answers, and answer the questions.

1. Check the responsibilities of the provincial/territorial government.

    ◯ hospitals   ◯ income tax

    ◯ liquor licence   ◯ education

    ◯ marriage licence   ◯ energy

    ◯ road signs and traffic ◯ relations with other countries

2. What is the title of the Queen's representative in:

    a. a province?   _____

    b. a territory?   _____

3. What does each of these consist of?

    a. the Legislature   _____

    b. the Cabinet   _____

4. How many years does a Premier govern for?

    _____

The Provincial/Territorial Government

A. **Read what these people say. Check the one that is talking about something "provincial/territorial".**

1. I work at an office that helps people get their marriage licence.

2. I'm a firefighter. I'm based in beautiful Muskoka, a cottage country in Ontario.

3. I'm a nurse. I work at a community health centre in the town of Ajax.

B. **Write "federal" or "provincial/territorial" for each of the following.**

1. Who is responsible for Canada's national mail carrier?

_____

2. Who is responsible for training Canadian soldiers?

_____

3.

Who is responsible for issuing our driver's licence?

_____

The Provincial/Territorial Government

Answer the following questions about your premier. Visit the website of your provincial/territorial government to help you. Then find and paste a picture of your premier in the box.

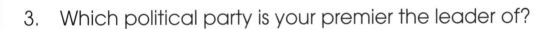

My Premier

1. Which province/territory do you live in?

   _____

2. Who is your premier?

   _____

3. Which political party is your premier the leader of?

   _____

4. Each premier also represents a riding. What is your premier's riding?

   _____

5. Find out some of the responsibilities of your premier and describe them.

   _____

   _____

   _____

   _____

The Provincial/Territorial Government

Read what Sally and Michael say and fill out your own information on the right. Then identify something in your riding that you would like your MLA/MPP/MHA/MNA to do. Write him or her a letter.

We live in Ontario. Our riding is York-Centre. Our MPP is Mr. Ken Dryden.

- My riding:

  _____

- My MLA/MPP/MHA/MNA:

  _____

- My province/territory:

  _____

Dear Mr./Ms. _____ :
your MLA/MPP/MHA/MNA

Thank you for doing such a great job of representing my riding. There is one thing, however, that I would like you to do for my riding, and that is

_____

_____

_____

_____ .

Sincerely,

_____
your name

The Provincial/Territorial Government

Look at Laura's drawing of the legislative building in her province. Make a trip to the legislative building(s) in your province or territory and make your own drawing.

My Drawing of the
Legislative Building(s) in

name of your province/territory

Inside the Legislative Chamber

In the legislative building of each province/territory, there is a room where members of the Legislative Assembly meet to debate and pass laws, called the "Chamber". Inside the Chamber, you will find the following:

Legislative Chamber

Lieutenant Governor or Commissioner
Queen's representative for the province/territory

Premier
head of the provincial/territorial government

Opposition Leader
leader of another party that is not the governing party

Members of the Legislative Assembly
people elected into the Assembly; called "MLAs" in most provinces/territories except Ontario (MPPs), Quebec (MNAs), and Newfoundland and Labrador (MHAs)

Clerk
Senior Officer who gives advice on parliamentary procedure

Speaker
"umpire" during parliamentary debates elected by other members

Sergeant-at-Arms
Officer responsible for securtiy

Mace
ceremonial staff symbolizing the Speaker's authority

Inside the Legislative Chamber

Across

A. "Queen" for the province: Lieutenant _____

B. responsible for the security of the Legislative Chamber

C. _____ party: not the governing party

D. head of the provincial/territorial government

E. the "umpire" during debates

Down

1. "Queen" for the territory

2. symbolizes the Speaker's authority

3. Senior Officer of the House

4. people elected to the Chamber: Members of the Legislative _____

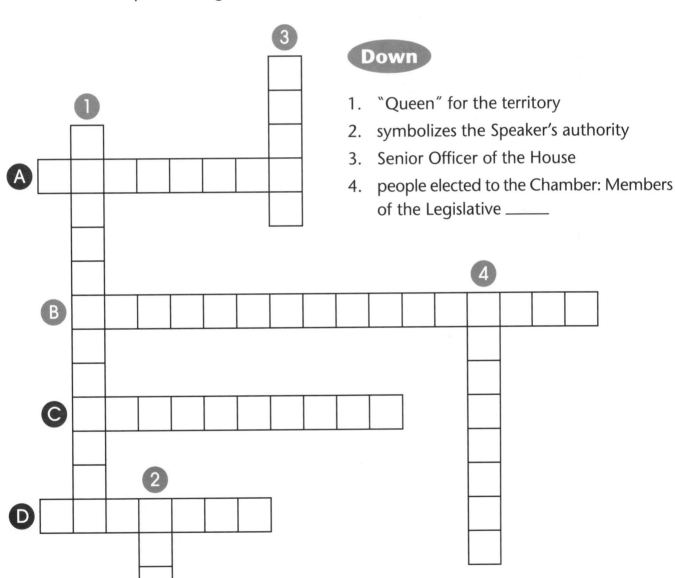

Inside the Legislative Chamber

Match the following with the descriptions.

1. Clerk • • symbol of the Speaker's authority

2. Premier • • responsible for security

3. Mace • • head of the provincial/territorial government

4. Lieutenant Governor • • Senior Officer of the Chamber

5. Members of the Legislative Assembly • • controls the debates inside the Chamber

6. Sergeant-at-Arms • • the Queen's representative for the province

7. Opposition Leader • • leader of a party that is not in power

8. Speaker • • the Queen's representative for the territory

9. Commissioner • • MLAs, MPPs, MNAs, MHAs

Inside the Legislative Chamber

Use the library and/or online resources to look for a picture of the Mace used in the Legislative Chamber of your province/territory. Make a sketch and then colour it.

Making Laws in a Province/Territory

Every law begins as an idea. When the idea is presented to the legislature, it is in the form of a "bill", which goes through several stages before becoming a law. All the members of the legislature have a chance to study the bill, give their opinions, and make suggestions to improve it. Here is a look at the process at the provincial/territorial level:

First Reading

This is when an MLA/MPP/MNA/MHA or a Cabinet Minister introduces the bill to the legislature. Think of this as the "rough draft" of a writing assignment. The other members then decide whether to discuss it further. If the answer is yes, the bill is assigned a number and scheduled for a second reading. Everyone gets a copy of the bill to study, but no debate is allowed yet.

Second Reading

This is when all the members of the legislature discuss the bill further to look at its pros and cons. They vote on whether or not to let it proceed to the next step.

Committee Stage

This is when a committee examines the bill, which can take days or months! There can be suggestions for changes for each section, and votes are taken. All the suggestions are then reported back to the legislature.

Third Reading

This is the last debate for the bill. Once it is over, the Speaker calls for a final vote on making it a law. If there is a majority, then the bill proceeds to the last step.

Royal Assent

This is the ceremonial stage where the Lieutenant Governor/Commissioner signs the bill and puts an official "seal" on it, giving it approval on behalf of the Queen. The bill is now a law, and the legislature chooses a date for the law to take effect.

Making Laws in a Province/Territory

A Simulation of the
Law-Making Process

Instructions for the Teacher:

1. *Brainstorm with your class for "bill" ideas. Then give each of your students a cue card. Ask them to put their names on the back. Tell them they are Members of the Legislative Assembly ("MLAs", "MPPs", "MHAs", or "MNAs"). Ask them to each come up with a bill and write it down.*

2. *Shuffle all the "bills" in a shoebox. Assign a group of students to be the "committee".*

3. *Randomly draw out a bill. Ask the Member who wrote it to read it in front of the class. This is the first reading, when the bill is introduced.*

4. *Take a vote and see if the majority wants the bill to have a second reading. If so, proceed to step 5. If not, this bill will not pass. Draw out another bill for the process.*

5. *This is the second reading. Let the Member tell the class why his or her bill is a good idea. Then have all Members debate what is good and bad about the bill. You are the Speaker, so decide whose turn it is to speak.*

6. *After a fair share of debate by everyone, take a vote to see if the majority wants the bill examined by the committee (from step 2). If so, go to step 7. If not, go on to step 11.*

7. *Allow members of the committee to improve the bill by making suggestions. Other Members may talk quietly amongst themselves in the meantime.*

8. *Have the committee hand in their suggestions. Read each suggestion to the class and take a vote. Keep the suggestions that a majority of Members agree upon.*

9. *This is the third reading. Read the improved bill to the class. Take a final vote. If the majority agrees to pass the bill, it goes to you the Lieutenant Governor/Commissioner.*

10. *As Lieutenant Governor/Commissioner, you approve of the bill by giving it Royal Assent.*

11. *Draw out another bill and repeat the process. Assign a different committee this time.*

The Municipal Government

What is a municipality? A municipality is a local community within a province or territory. Every municipality has its own government to take care of local matters, which affect the daily lives of its citizens.

Here are some of the responsibilities of the municipal government:

 Utilities like water   **Parks and recreation**

 Property taxes   **Public transit**

 Snow removal   **Garbage collection**

 Roads and street lights   **Local police and fire protection**

 Vehicle, bicycle, and pedestrian traffic

There are different types of municipalities:

Rural Municipality – no minimum population requirement

Village – 100 or more residents and 50 or more homes/businesses

Town – 500 or more residents

City – 5000 or more residents

Just like how the federal government has the House of Commons and provincial/ territorial governments have legislative assemblies, municipalities have local councils, made up of people elected by the community. Each local council is headed by a Mayor (or Reeve for a village), and is made up of City Councillors, who hold meetings at City Hall to pass **bylaws***.

* The word "by" comes from language of the Vikings, meaning "town" or "village", so "bylaw" means "town law".

The Municipal Government

A. Write "T" for "True" or "F" for "False".

1. City Councillors make up part of the municipal government.   _____

2. The head of a municipal government is the Mayor or Reeve.   _____

3. The Royal Ontario Museum, located in Toronto, is the
    responsibility of the City of Toronto.   _____

4. Sales tax such as the GST is collected by the municipal
    government.   _____

5. Property tax from homeowners and land owners is collected
    by the municipal government.   _____

6. A "village" is a municipality that has between 100 and 500
    residents.   _____

B. Complete the following sentences.

1. The Premier is to a province/territory what the _____ is to
    a city.

2. A law is to a province/territory what a _____ is to a town.

3. The House of Commons is to Canada what the _____ is
    to a city.

The Municipal Government

A. Fill in the blanks to complete this article.

> law   town   right   province   Ontario   government

Monday, January 14, 2008.

Mayor helps the environment!

By Wendy Sharma
staff reporter

In the *1.*_____ of Aurora, there are areas where homeowners are not allowed to hang their laundry on a clothesline because it is against the *2.*_____ . It has been made illegal because some people think it is an eyesore to the neighbourhood.

But everyone should have the *3.*_____ to dry their clothes outside and save energy, so Phyllis Morris, the mayor of Aurora since 2006, brought the issue to the Ontario *4.*_____ by launching the "Right to Dry" campaign in August of 2007.

She received support from the Conservation Council of *5.*_____ and the World Wildlife Fund of Canada. Her campaign even made it to the news.

Word got to Ontario's chief energy conservation officer, Peter Love, who recommended Morris's idea to the *6.*_____ . After all, a standard clothes dryer creates up to 840 kg of air pollution and greenhouse gases every year.

And so by January of this year, Ontario's Minister of Energy made a promise to lift the ban on the humble clothesline. See how big a difference a mayor from a small town can make?

B. Give a detailed opinion to each of the following.

1. Some people think that having laundry on a clothesline is an eyesore. Do you think so? Why or why not?

_____

_____

_____

_____

_____

2. Do you think that a ban on using the clothesline to hang your laundry is a violation of your rights? Why or why not?

_____

_____

_____

_____

3. Think of something that your community can improve upon. What would you like the mayor to do to make the community better?

_____

_____

_____

_____

You Can Suggest a New Bylaw, Too!

Everyone can make a difference in their community! If you think your village, city, or town needs improvement, you can get involved in a number of ways: plant a tree, volunteer at a shelter for the homeless, participate at local meetings, or even suggest a new bylaw!

Here's how it works: take the City of Toronto, for example. Toronto has a recycling program for paper products, cans, and bottles, but if you think the program should include more recyclable materials, you can contact your city councillor about it.

If the councillor thinks the idea is good, he or she may bring it up during council meetings. Staff at City Hall will then do research on it, get advice and feedback from different people, and consider different ways that could make the idea work. If their research shows that the idea can be made into reality, then the staff will write a report on it.

Afterwards, the report will go to a committee or community council to be reviewed, where members will discuss its pros and cons. This is also the stage where people from the public like yourself can make presentations about the idea. If the majority of members in the committee or community council think the report is good, they will give it to City Council for consideration.

City Council will hold meetings to discuss the report. If the majority of city councillors agree with the idea presented in the report, then they make it into a **bylaw**, which is a law in the city that citizens will have to follow.

You can Make a Difference!

Your idea

↓

City Councillor

↓ Council meeting

Staff at City Hall

↓ Report

A committee/ community council

↓ Review

City Council

↓ More discussions

Bylaw

You Can Suggest a New Bylaw, Too!

A. Write 1 to 5 to put the following steps in order.

How a New Bylaw is Made

◯ The city councillor brings the citizen's idea to council meetings.

◯ Staff at City Hall do research on the idea and write a report on it.

◯ The report is reviewed by a committee or community council.

◯ A citizen has a new idea to improve the city, so he or she contacts the city councillor about it.

◯ The report is discussed in a council meeting and put to a vote, and if most of the councillors think it is a great idea, then it is made into a bylaw.

B. Answer the following questions.

1. If you have an idea to improve your city, who can you contact?

_____

2. If you want to make a presentation about your idea, at which stage can you do so?

_____

3. What does an idea become if it is approved by city council?

_____

You Can Suggest a New Bylaw, Too!

Come up with some ideas to make your community a better place to live. Then "make up" a bylaw that could turn each idea into reality.

1. **Idea:** It would be better if everyone could produce less garbage.

   Bylaw: Only two or fewer bags of garbage will be collected from each household on garbage collection day.

2. **Idea:** It would be better if more people walked or took public transit instead of driving their cars.

   Bylaw: Make the city less car-friendly by putting a limited number of parking spaces per area in the city.

3. **Idea:** _____

   _____

   Bylaw: _____

   _____

4. **Idea:** _____

   _____

   Bylaw: _____

   _____

You Can Suggest a New Bylaw, Too!

Read what Andrea says to complete this activity.

One way to improve your community is to prepare a "petition" like the one below. Identify a problem in your school or neighbourhood. Write it down on the petition below and gather people who support your view. Ask them for their names, addresses, contact information, and signatures.

We, the undersigned, recognize the following problem:

_____

_____

We would like to fix it by _____

_____

Name	Address	Phone Number	Signature

Grades **4-6**

Project Ideas

Michaëlle Jean
Canada's First Black Governor General

Her Excellency the Right Honourable Michaëlle Jean is the first Black Governor General in Canada. Her responsibilities include visiting Canadians from coast to coast to promote national identity, and visiting foreign countries to build friendships with them.

But what has been her life story? Find out all the interesting details of her life. Use the following to help you do your research:

Guiding Questions

- Where was she born?
- Why did she and her family come to Canada?
- What did she study?
- What was her job before she became Governor General?

You may use a bristol board or large piece of construction paper to paste different pieces of information. You may also make a booklet. You can illustrate your information with pictures as well.

When you have finished putting together your poster/booklet, present it to the rest of the class!

Lester B. Pearson
World's Problem Solver

You can think of Lester B. Pearson as Superman: during his term as Prime Minister from 1963 to 1968, Pearson oversaw the introduction of the Canada Pension Plan, universal Medicare, the Commission on bilingualism and biculturalism, and the birth of the Maple Leaf Flag. Few other prime ministers had done so much in so little time as Pearson did.

But what has been his life story? Find out all the interesting details of his life. Use the following to help you do your research:

Guiding Questions

- Where was he born?
- What did he do in World War II?
- What was his job before becoming Prime Minister?
- Why is Pearson known for being a peacekeeper?

You may use a bristol board or large piece of construction paper to paste different pieces of information. You may also make a "book". You can illustrate your information with pictures as well.

When you have finished putting together your poster/book, present it to the rest of the class!

James Bartleman
Ontario's First Aboriginal Lieutenant Governor

From living near a dump in Muskoka to being the Queen's representative for Ontario – that is what a Native kid named James Bartleman did! Find out how he got there and what he did in his career by using the following in your research:

Guiding Questions

- Where did he live as a child?
- What was his neighbourhood like as he was growing up?
- What did he do after graduating from university?
- As Lieutenant Governor, how did he help other Aboriginal children?

You may use a bristol board or large piece of construction paper to paste different pieces of information. You may also make a booklet. You can illustrate your information with pictures as well.

When you have finished putting together your poster/booklet, present it to the rest of the class!

Tommy Douglas
Social Policy Innovator

You don't necessarily have to be the Prime Minister to transform the country. Take Tommy Douglas, for example, a man with a fiery public-speaking talent and an extraordinary commitment to his country who was never Prime Minister, and yet changed the lives of so many Canadians for the better.

Find out how he did so by using the following:

Guiding Questions

- How did he help the common people in Depression-era Saskatchewan?
- Douglas became Premier for Saskatchewan. What was his political party?
- What was the mission of Douglas's political party?
- He was re-elected as Premier many times. How come?
- What was his "great idea"? What famous name did Canadians call him as a result?

You may use a bristol board or large piece of construction paper to paste different pieces of information. You may also make a booklet. You can illustrate your information with pictures as well.

When you have finished putting together your poster/booklet, present it to the rest of the class!

Ken Dryden
Hockey Player-Turned MP

You may have seen Ken Dryden in the news: he is Member of Parliament representing the region of York Centre in Ontario. But as far as politicians go, Ken Dryden has been many things: lawyer, businessman, author, TV commentator, and NHL goaltender. He won six Stanley Cups with the Montreal Canadiens in the 1970s and was named to the Hockey Hall of Fame in 1983.

Find out about the interesting NHL background of this Ontario MP. Use the following in your research:

Guiding Questions

- Where did he play hockey as a university student?
- What was his team when he played hockey in Canada?
- What was the title of his first book?
- Which of his books was about what hockey says about the Canadian society?

You may use a bristol board or large piece of construction paper to paste different pieces of information. You may also make a booklet. You can illustrate your information with pictures as well.

When you have finished putting together your poster/booklet, present it to the rest of the class!

Quebec: a Francophone Province

> *Quebec is the only Canadian province that has a mainly Francophone population. Because of its distinctiveness, it is the only province recognized by the Canadian government as a "nation".*

Learn as much as you can about Quebec and design a giant travel brochure. Use library books and the Internet. You can even visit your local travel agencies to ask for tourist information. The guides they provide may help you get ideas.

You may use a bristol board or large piece of construction paper to paste different pieces of information. You can illustrate your information with pictures as well.

When you have finished putting together your travel brochure, present it to the rest of the class!

How a Mayor is Helping Her Community Save Energy

You don't have to be the Minister of Environment at the provincial/territorial or federal level to make a difference to the environment. You could be the mayor of a small town and make a huge difference by helping your community save energy!

That's what Phyllis Morris, the mayor of Aurora since 2006, did by launching the "Right to Dry" campaign in August of 2007. In some parts of Aurora, it is against the law to hang laundry on a clothesline because some people think it's an eyesore. Everyone should have the right to dry their clothes outside and save energy, however, so Mayor Morris brought the issue to the Ontario government.

Search the Internet to find out what has happened since then, providing a list of events along with dates. Use the following to help you:

Keywords

- Phyllis Morris
- Aurora
- Right to Dry campaign
- Conservation Council of Ontario
- World Wildlife Fund of Canada

You may use a bristol board or large piece of construction paper to paste different pieces of information. You may also make a booklet. You can illustrate your information with pictures as well.

When you have finished putting together your poster/booklet, present it to the rest of the class!

Grades 4-6

Tests, Self-Evaluation, and Answers

Test One:

Overview of the Canadian Government

A. Circle the correct answers.

1. Canada is a federation, a democracy, and a _____ monarchy.

   A. federal   B. provincial   C. constitutional

2. Before an immigrant becomes a Canadian citizen, he or she takes an _____ of Citizenship.

   A. Oath   B. Song   C. Anthem

3. In Canada, there are three levels of government: federal, provincial, and _____ .

   A. village   B. town   C. municipal

4. In order for a political party to govern a province or territory, it needs to win the provincial/territorial _____ .

   A. riding   B. election   C. country

5. This is the extra money we pay whenever we buy things: _____ .

   A. income tax   B. sales tax   C. property tax

6. The _____ is the highest court in Canada.

   A. Federal Court of Appeal

   B. Tax Court of Canada

   C. Supreme Court of Canada

B. Fill in the blanks.

1. There are ten provinces and three _____ in Canada.

2. The head of the federal government is the _____ .

3. An organization of members that want to be the government of a province/territory or the country is called a _____ .

4. *The* _____ *of Rights and Freedoms* protects the rights and freedoms of Canadian citizens.

5. In Canada, the person who represents the Queen is called the _____ .

6. English and _____ are the two official languages in Canada.

C. Answer these questions in complete sentences.

1. What are some responsibilities of the federal government?

   _____

   _____

2. Name two political parties in Canada.

   _____

   _____

3. Name some of the services that you get by paying taxes.

   _____

   _____

Test Two:
The Federal, Provincial/Territorial, and Municipal Governments

A.   Circle the correct answers.

1.   In a territorial government, the Queen's representative is the _____ .

  A. Commissioner   B. Lieutenant Governor   C. Mayor

2.   The head of a province/territory is the _____ .

  A. Mayor   B. Prime Minister   C. Premier

3.   Before a bill becomes law in a province/territory, it must be approved by the Lieutenant Governor/Commissioner in a ceremony called _____ .

  A. Royal Assent   B. Third Reading   C. Committee

4.   Inside the legislative chamber, the ceremonial staff that symbolizes the Speaker's authority is the _____ .

  A. Sergeant   B. Royal Assent   C. Mace

5.   MLA stands for Member of _____ Assembly.

  A. Legislative   B. Legislature   C. Loyal

6.   The head of the municipal government is the _____ .

  A. Trustee   B. City Councillor   C. Mayor

76

B. Fill in the blanks.

1. The House of Commons is where _____ (MPs) meet to discuss and make new laws.

2. In the federal government, the "upper house" is the _____ .

3. When an MLA or Cabinet Minister introduces a bill in the legislative chamber, the process is called _____ .

4. When a municipality has over 5000 residents, it is called a _____ .

5. In a municipal election, we elect a Mayor, City Councillors, and _____ .

C. Answer these questions in complete sentences.

1. What are some responsibilities of the provincial/territorial government?

_____

_____

2. What are some responsibilities of the municipal government?

_____

_____

3. Which tax is collected by the municipal government?

_____

_____

Self-Evaluation

1. I can explain what a constitutional monarchy is.

2. I can identify the three levels of government in Canada: federal, provincial/territorial, and municipal.

3. I know what the head of government is at each level: Prime Minister (federal), Premier (provincial/territorial), and Mayor or Reeve (municipal).

4. I can name some examples of political parties in Canada.

5. I know that we have elections at every level of government.

6. I know that the Supreme Court of Canada is the highest court in the Canadian justice system.

7. I can talk about some responsibilities of the federal, provincial/territorial, and municipal governments.

8. I know that the House of Commons is the major law-making body in the federal government; it is where Members of Parliament (MPs) meet to discuss and pass laws.

9. I know that each province/territory has its own legislative chamber, where Members of Legislative Assembly (MLAs) meet to discuss and pass laws.

10. I can name some important symbols in the provincial/territorial Legislative Chamber and in the House of Commons, like the Speaker and the Mace.

11. I know what a "bill" is: a draft of a proposed law.

12. I understand what happens in the law-making process.

Answers

p. 7

A. 1. B 2. C
3. A 4. D

B. 1. It is a country where the monarch is the head of state, but whose powers are limited by the laws of the country.
2. The role of the monarch is mostly symbolic, to carry out traditional and ceremonial duties.
3. Its purpose is to protect the basic rights and freedoms of all Canadians.

p. 8

BC: British Columbia QB: Quebec
AB: Alberta
NFL: Newfoundland and Labrador
SK: Saskatchewan PEI: Prince Edward Island
MB: Manitoba NB: New Brunswick
ON: Ontario NS: Nova Scotia
YT: Yukon NT: Northwest Territories
NU: Nunavut ten ; three

p. 11

A. 1. F 2. T 3. T
4. F 5. T

B. 1. provincial/territorial 2. federal
3. municipal (individual examples)

p. 13

A. 1. sales tax 2. property tax 3. income tax
B. (in any order)
1. health care 2. education
3. social assistance 4. parks and recreation

p. 14

1a. safety b. sidewalks c. street lights
2a. recreation b. books

p. 17

1. an organization with the goal of forming a government
2. win votes from the population
3. Canada will have a Liberal government
4. has a diverse population with a variety of viewpoints
5. then it means the New Democratic Party has won the federal election

p. 18 (Individual pictures and writing)

2. Liberal Party 3. Liberal Party 4. Green Party

p. 21

1. riding 2. ward

3. Prime Minister 4. Premier
5. MLAs 6. MPPs
7. School Trustees 8. municipal

p. 25

1. Federal Court
2. Provincial/Territorial Superior Courts
3. Provincial Courts
4. Supreme Court of Canada
5. Federal Court of Appeal
6. Provincial Courts of Appeal
7. Tax Court of Canada

p. 27

1. responsibility ; protecting the environment
2. right ; mobility rights
3. freedom ; freedom of religion
4. responsibility ; obeying Canadian laws

p. 28

1. A 2. A 3. B
4. B 5. B

p. 29

1. faithful 2. true 3. Queen
4. Queen 5. laws 6. citizen

p. 30

1. native 2. love 3. hearts
4. North 5. free 6. wide
7. guard 8. glorious

p. 33

1. Prime Minister 2. Ottawa
3. federal 4. Senate
5. Cabinet 6. executive
7. legislative 8. Sovereign

p. 34

1. John A. Macdonald
2. William Lyon Mackenzie King
3. Lester B. Pearson 4. Kim Campbell
5. Jeanne Sauvé 6. Cairine Wilson
7. Agnes Macphail 8. Liberal Party
9. Liberal Party

p. 35

A. ENVIRONMENT B. HEALTH
C. RESOURCES D. IMMIGRATION
E. SOCIAL F. HERITAGE

Answers

1. JUSTICE   2. INTERNATIONAL

p. 37

1. House of Commons   2. Senate
3. Speaker   4. Official Opposition
5. Opposition Members   6. Mace

p. 38

A. Speaker ; controls the debates
B. Mace ; symbolizes the Speaker's authority
C. Prime Minister ; head of the government
D. Government Members ; members of the political party in power
E. Leader of the Official Opposition ; leader of the party with the second-highest number of seats
F. Opposition Members ; members of the party with the second-highest number of seats

p. 39 (Individual drawing)

the Speaker's authority ; at every meeting of the MPs in the House of Commons

p. 41

1. It is the rough draft of an idea before it becomes law.
2. It is the review procedure that every bill goes through before becoming law.
3. The bill is discussed and debated in the legislature.
4a. House of Commons   b. Legislative Assembly
  c. Town Hall/City Hall
5. It goes through three readings. At the first reading, a bill is introduced to the legislature.

p. 45

1. hospitals ; liquor licence ; education ; marriage licence ; energy
2a. Lieutenant Governor   b. Commissioner
3a. MLAs/MPPs   b. Ministers
4. A Premier governs for up to five years.

p. 46

A. 1. ✔
B. 1. federal   2. federal
  3. provincial/territorial

p. 51

A. GOVERNOR   B. SERGEANT-AT-ARMS
C. OPPOSITION   D. PREMIER
E. SPEAKER   1. COMMISSIONER
2. MACE   3. CLERK
4. ASSEMBLY

p. 52

1. Senior Officer of the Chamber
2. head of the provincial/territorial government
3. symbol of the Speaker's authority
4. the Queen's representative for the province
5. MLAs, MPPs, MNAs, MHAs
6. responsible for security
7. leader of a party that is not in power
8. controls the debates inside the Chamber
9. the Queen's representative for the territory

p. 57

A. 1. T   2. T   3. F
  4. F   5. T   6. T
B. 1. Mayor   2. bylaw   3. City Council

p. 58

A. 1. town   2. law   3. right
  4. government   5. Ontario   6. province

p. 61

A. 2 ; 3 ; 4 ; 1 ; 5
B. 1. I can contact my city councillor.
2. I can make a presentation when the idea is being reviewed by a committee or community council.
3. It becomes a bylaw.

Test One

A. 1. C   2. A   3. C
  4. B   5. B   6. C
B. 1. territories   2. Prime Minister
  3. political party   4. Charter
  5. Governor General   6. French
C. (Suggested answers)
1. Some responsibilities are the environment, citizenship and immigration, and income tax.
2. Two parties are the Liberal Party and the Green Party.
3. They are health care, education, social assistance, and recreation.

Test Two

A. 1. A   2. C   3. A
  4. C   5. A   6. C
B. 1. Members of Parliament   2. Senate
  3. first reading   4. city
  5. School Trustees
C. (Suggested answers)
1. Some of them are hospitals, the police, and education.
2. Some of them are roads, street lights, and parks.
3. It is the property tax.

      Canadian Government | G.4-6